PENGUIN BOOKS

Steve Bell was born in London in 1951. His
formative years were spent in Slough, Bucks (now
Berks) where he attended the Grammar School.
Later he studied Fine Art at Teesside College of Art
and Leeds University. After graduating he worked as
a teacher in Birmingham but the call of the nib was
too strong and he soon shot to fame with his
'Maxwell the Mutant' strip in the now deceased
Birmingham alternative paper 'Broadside'. Thus
encouraged he threw up his teaching job to work as a
freelance cartoonist and illustrator. His work has
featured in 'New Society', 'Social Work Today',
numerous childrens' magazines and comics, and in
'The Leveller' where 'Lord God Almighty' appeared.
He now produces a daily cartoon strip called 'If...' in
the Guardian.

   'Maggie's Farm', published as a Penguin in 1981,
first started appearing in London's Time Out in 1979,
and has continued since in City Limits. Steve Bell is
married, has one child and lives in Brighton.

Further Down on MAGGIE'S FARM AND OTHER STORIES

STEVE BELL

PENGUIN BOOKS

Penguin Books Ltd, Harmondsworth, Middlesex, England
Penguin Books, 625 Madison Avenue, New York, New York 10022, U.S.A.
Penguin Books Australia Ltd, Ringwood, Victoria, Australia
Penguin Books Canada Ltd, 2801 John Street, Markham, Ontario, Canada L3R 1B4
Penguin Books (N.Z.) Ltd, 182-190 Wairau Road, Auckland 10, New Zealand

First published by Not, City Limits, The Leveller, The Guardian 1980, 1981, 1982
Published in Penguin Books 1982

Made and printed in Great Britain
Set in Bell Bold and Souvenir

ISBN 0 14 00.6417 6

Designed by Brian Homer
Edited by Steve Bell and Brian Homer

CONTENTS

Thanks to Heather, Brian, Duncan and William
for help sorting things out.

INTRODUCTION

If you are pausing in a shop, uncertain whether or not to buy this book; or alone in the bathroom at the party of someone you hardly know; or a member of Customs and Excise in some country that is not Britain, and you are about to examine the contents of this book – then, bully for all of you.

Presumably you want to know whether you should buy, read or seize this. Potential buyers should know that the book's author, cartoonist Steve Bell, has a small son, Bill, who will remain small unless the royalties come through on this volume. Lonely party-goers might like to know that by perusing Bell they will join the ranks of the readers of City Limits and The Leveller magazine and a newspaper called The Guardian. And Customs Officers should be referred to two episodes of Maggie's Farm: the first involves a Cabinet Minister whose first name is Keith, the second features a Prime Minister, a chain saw and a lamb. Suffice to say that these episodes feature two forms of misbehaviour which are very seriously regarded in Britain – public nudity and wasting one's food.

This is Volume Two of Maggie's Farm. Unlike Jaws Two, Godfather Two, Superman Two and Leviticus Two, this is possibly *even better* than Maggie's Farm One.

Not only is there a full set of Maggie's Farms complete with all the recent horrors – recession, riots, the nuclear threat, the Falklands Crisis, Norman Tebbit – but there is more besides. In his cartoon strip, Lord God Almighty, Bell pays homage to the old canard (or 'tribute to the old duck,' as we say in English) that God moves in a mysterious way. And with his other strip, 'If...', he bends the knee to that marvellous Kipling verse engraved in the hearts of generations of schoolchildren: 'If...I loved you, Words would not come in an easy way...'

So. Shopper, buy this book and give the shop-assistant one of those wan smiles of yours that you practise in the reflections of supermarket windows; party-goer, hide the book and adjust your dress; Customs Officer, stay your hand. The rest of you – read on.

Duncan Campbell
News Editor, City Limits

Foreword by Douglas the Dissident Dog:

I'M A DOG. I'VE BEEN A DOG ALL MY LIFE, AND I KNOW WHAT I'M TALKING ABOUT!

"In this International Year of the Dog, a few facts about Dogs:

FACT: More money is now spent on Dogs in the time it takes you to read this than it would take to feed every living creature, including the goats, for the next fifteen years.

FACT: Dogs are cringing, violent, smelly, fundamentally unreliable, and produce nothing you would wish to touch with a barge pole.

FACT: Dogs are notoriously slow-witted, yet today the Great Powers all have Dogs in the highest positions of responsibility.

FACT: Advancing Dogware Technology means that Dogs now have the ability to wipe out all forms of life on this planet.

HAIG

"There is a gap in the annals of Maggies Farm extending from where Volume One left off with the fall of Giscard and Horace in May 1981, through to October '81, where the weekly chronicle recommences with the interview between Our Leader and the hard-hitting Antipodean Oaf, Bruce Kanga. This gap is largely the result of newtish machinations attending the birth of the All-Animal mag-azine 'CITY LIMITS' in which Maggies Farm now appears.

If you cast your mind back to the time of the Thatcher/Zombie junta's second anniversary, you may recall a widely publicised mass-subscription fertility rite: the wedding between the owner's son, Dog-impersonator, Charles, born-to-be-Rex, and an approved child-bearing unit.

You may also remember the big thing among patriotic youth demonstrating it's loyalty to Crown, Church and Monetary System throughout that summer: the Riots.

And who could forget the prolonged struggle between Hedgehog Benn and the Healeybun.

All these things Maggies Farm managed mainly to miss, though they do receive some attention in the special pull-out blasphemous section in the middle of this volume.

Anyway, it all pales into insignificance in comparison with the ever-proliferating Dog Threat. Even as I write the Dogs are at it again in the South Atlantic. Surely, things have gone far enough?? To echo the words of a famous, though admittedly Dead Dog, Gen. Charles De Gaulle: "Pas un chien-lit!" We must ask ourselves: is this a healthy Society, or is this merely a Dog's Nest??"

Maggie's Farm

COURT CIRCULAR

Just why is BREEDING so important?

FIRSTLY, IT IS A QUESTION OF ONE'S GENES; THAT MECHANISM BY WHICH THE BEST + MOST SUCCESSFUL CHARACTERISTICS ARE TRANSMITTED FROM GENERATION TO GENERATION. IF ONE CAN CLAIM DIRECT DESCENT FROM, SAY, ERIC BLOODAXE....

ARCHETYPAL OUTDOOR TYPE

..THEN ONE CAN BE FAIRLY SURE ONE'S GOING TO BE PRETTY ACCEPTABLE SOCIALLY.

THUS THE MOST IMPORTANT THING IS TO KNOW WHO ONE'S FOREBEARS ARE..

NO... BUT SERIOUSLY, THIS IS THE ONLY WAY ONE CAN BE CERTAIN THAT ONE IS:

a) NOT BLACK

b) NOT JEWISH

c) NOT IRISH

d) NOT A RED INDIAN

e) NOT A MEMBER OF THE COMMONIST PARTY

f) NOT A CATHOLIC

AND SO ON.......

THIS ACCOUNTS FOR ONE'S SUBLIME SELF-ASSURANCE WHEN ONE IS A MEMBER OF A ROYAL FAMILY.

ON THE POSITIVE SIDE, ONE IS ALSO ASSURED OF CERTAIN PHYSICAL + INTELLECTUAL QUALITIES. FOR EXAMPLE:

THE HAPSBURG LIP...

YOU *@☆!※!!*! LOWLIFE ASSHOLES! I'M GONNA CRAP ON YOU ALL, YOU SCUM!

...THE BOURBON BISCUIT....

CHOFF...URP.... LET THEM EAT CAKE... ...BELCH...CHOMP..

...AND THE HOHENZOLLERN OUTWARD-BOUND TENDENCY....

INVADE BELGIUM NOW!!

MAGGIE'S FARM

MAGGIE'S FARM

S.Bell

SAATCHI
NICE LADY

SADLY, MARGARET YOUR POPULARITY IS NO LONGER WHAT IT WAS...

...NEVERTHELESS WE SHOULD TRY TO LOOK ON THE POSITIVE SIDE...

HMMM

...THIS LATEST POLL SHOWS CONCLUSIVELY THAT YOU'RE MORE POPULAR THAN ANTHRAX...

YES, YES

...AND THIS POLL DEMONSTRATES CLEARLY THAT AT LEAST 62·8% OF CONSERVATIVE VOTERS WOULD ACTUALLY PREFER TO BE SMALL PILES OF RADIOACTIVE DUST.

GOOD, GOOD!

BUT, BASICALLY, MARGARET, WE'VE GOT TO DO SOMETHING TO IMPROVE YOUR "RAH-FACTOR" PRETTY DAMN QUICK!

MY "RAH FACTOR"... IS THAT ONE OF YOUR CURIOUS MARKETING CONCEPTS?

IN A WAY MARGARET.

...WE'LL FIGHT THEM ON THE BEACHES!! RAH! RAH! RAH!

RAH! RAH! RAH!

THEY MAY CALL US MANIACS, BUT WE KNOW WE'RE BRITISH MANIACS!!

RAH! RAH! RAH! RAH! RAH! RAH!

BLOOD, TOIL TEARS, SWEAT, RUBBER, CHURCHILL'S TROUSERS!!

RAH! RAH!

POUND RAH POUND

RAH!

CRUSH THE BLEEDING-HEART HEATHITE REVISIONIST SCUM BENEATH AN IRON HEEL!!

RAH! RAH! RAH! RAH!

WALLOP THE WEARY WILLIES!!

SMASH

THERE IS NO ALTERNATIVE!

RAH!

RAH! RAH! RAH! RAH! RAH! RAH!

RAH! RAH! RAH!

THIS IS BEYOND OUR WILDEST DREAMS!

SHE'S SMASHED ALL PREVIOUS RECORDS!

RAH! RAH! RAH!

BIG BOY

RAH! RAH!

© Noel Ternative ~ 1981.

Maggie's Farm

~ THE NUMBERS GAME ~

22

SDP? Maggie's Farm

28

29

Maggie's Farm

Maggie's Farm

AT THE RUGBY INTERNATIONAL BETWEEN THE WILD COLONIAL BLOCKHEADS XV AND THE PUBLIC SCHOOL OAFS ELITE XV....

RAH! RAH!

NUURGH!

URG

IGGH

YIKYIKYIK! MUST SET EXAMPLE TO YOUTH!

KEITH? ARE YOU FEELING QUITE ALRIGHT?

RIP!

SELL ALL PLAYING FIELDS TO PROPERTY DEVELOPERS NOW!!!

KEITH!! COME BACK!

JUST LOOK AT THAT!

POP! FLASH! KLIK!

ALL STATE SCHOOL TEACHERS ARE INEFFECTIVE!!

AMAZING!

SACK ALL INEFFECTIVE TEACHERS NOW!!

I'VE NEVER SEEN ANYTHING LIKE IT!!

FLASH!

FLASH!

KLIK, KLIK!

O.K., EASY NOW SUNSHINE!

PUT 'EM AWAY NOW!

I THINK I'VE GOT MY MESSAGE ACROSS AT LAST, MAG!

THAT WAS CERTAINLY A NOVEL METHOD, KEITH...

BUT, SADLY:

Daily Mail

NO NIPPLES! AND IT'S ALL THANKS TO FREE ENTERPRISE SAYS KE...

DAILY EXPRESS

NIPPLES?— WHAT ARE THEY? says

THE TAMER

Nipple-less Education Secretary may be an Extra-Terrestria

Sun BINGO BINGO BINGO

MAN WITH NO NIPPLES

IN STREAK SENSATION

Crazy Keith, an education secretary flummoxed fans at a rugby international yesterday with a nipple-free Flash.

Daily Mirror BINGO BOOBY PRIZE

NIPPLE-LESS NUDE STREAK SHOCK

"Making boobs is my business," said Keith, an education secretary, "and I make a lot."

NO-NIPPLE NUDE WON'T LOSE JOB AFTER ALL

His boss, MRS. THATCHER revealed today. "When Keith took a day off giving an excuse, and then Bared his All, I thought it was the last straw, but now I H understan...

31

32

33

34

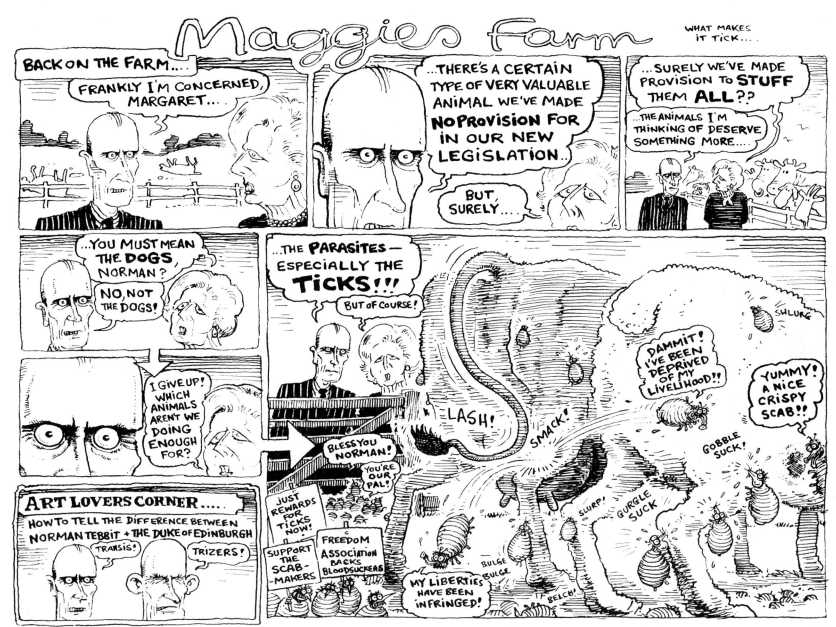

MAGGIE'S FARM

SINGALONGA THATCHAWHELP AND NORMAN*

Y'KNOW, WHELP— I GET MORE + MORE NOSTALGIC FOR THE 30's

AH YES NORM! THE 1930s WERE YEARS OF ENTERPRISE AND PRIDE IN EMPIRE!!

1930s? I'M TALKING ABOUT THE 1830s!!

GET UP OFF YOUR ARSES...

* SUNG TO THE TUNE OF "UNDERNEATH THE ARCHES"

...YOU USELESS BUNCH OF SHITS...

...BRITISH WORKING CLASSES...

...YOU REALLY ARE THE PITS....

...FECKLESS MOANING MINNIES.....

...AND NAMBY PAMBY REDS....

...GET UP OFF YOUR ARSES.....

OR I'LL CAVE IN YOUR HEADS!!

* GET YOUR ARSE ON YOUR BIKE GET YOUR ARSE ON YOUR BIKE GET ON YOUR BIKE....

* SUNG TO THE TUNE OF "GOD SAVE OUR GRACIOUS QUEEN"

42

44

50

DUCK DESIGNED BY B.J.HOMER

55

LORD GOD ALMIGHTY

HOLY WATER CANNON

FUEL HOLY WATER

"And God created lamposts...."

The following appeared in the 'LEVELLER' magazine during 1980 and 1981.

—LORD GOD ALMIGHTY——

ABSOLUTE + TOTAL COPYRIGHT © CHURCH OF THE PRIME TIME SELF HELP QUIK SAVE·O·MAT ® TINKER BELL 1980.

—LORD GOD ALMIGHTY—

LORD GOD ALMIGHTY

© TOTAL + COMPLETE (NO SHIT-THIS INCLUDES T-SHIRTS, RUBBER TOYS, UNIFORMS, EVERYTHING) TINKER BELL

UNIVERSAL COPYRIGHT © THE BOOK OF MILTON FRIEDEGG - 1981 -

WHAT'S ALL THIS JUNK ABOUT MOONIES, GABE?? WHAT THE FUCK ARE MOONIES ANYWAY??

THEY'RE A RIVAL CONGLOMERATE BASED IN THE FAR EAST... ...BASICALLY JUST A BUNCH OF PUNKS...

MOONIES CHARITABLE STATUS IN QUESTION

MOONIE MOONIE MOONIE

...THEIR BONA-FIDE CHARITABLE TAX-FREE STATUS IS IN QUESTION... ...ALLEGATIONS OF BRAINWASHING ...THAT KIND OF STUFF....

SERVES THE CHEEKY PUNKS RIGHT, GABE MAKE 'EM PAY THAT'S WHAT I SAY!

...SHIT, GABE... SOME OF THESE FUCKERS WILL BELIEVE ANY-THING!!

WE ARE MOONIES RAVING MOONIES

FLOP!

INLAND REVENUE
THE ONE TRUE LORD GOD ALMIGHTY POSTE RESTANTE JERUSALEM
TAX DEMAND
PLEASE FORWARD

LORD GOD ALMIGHTY — THE FACTS

GOOD NEWS, GABE — THOSE GODLESS COMMIE-PUNK-DARWINISTS ARE ON THE RETREAT! THERE'S JUST A COUPLE OF MINOR DOCTRINAL POINTS I'D LIKE TO CLARIFY....GIMME A HOT LINE TO THE EDUCATION DEPT.....

THE PLAIN TRUTH
CREATIONISM TO BE GIVEN MORE EMPHASIS IN U.S. SCHOOLS.....
DARWIN OUT WORD OF GOD IN

REPEAT AFTER ME.... ON THE FIRST DAY, GOD CREATED THE MARKET FORCE.......

ON THE FIRST DAY, GOD CREATED THE MARKET FORCE...

ON THE SECOND DAY HE CREATED THE MONEY SUPPLY; ON THE THIRD DAY HE CREATED THE BANKS; ON THE FOURTH DAY HE CREATED THE I.M.F. ON THE FIFTH DAY HE CREATED MISCELLANEOUS OFFSHORE INVESTMENT FACILITIES..... ON THE SIXTH DAY HE CREATED MILTON FRIEDMAN.....

...ON THE SIXTH DAY HE CREATED MILTON FRIEDMAN.

...AND HE LOOKED DOWN AND HE SAW THAT IT WAS GOOD...

HAVEN'T YOU OMITTED SOME-THING, LORD?

...AND ON THE SEVENTH DAY HE CREATED HEAVEN, EARTH, THE OCEANS, THE FORESTS THE BIRDS OF THE AIR, THE BEASTS OF THE FIELD, MANKIND, AND ALL THE OTHER SHIT.....

64

65

GOD IS ON A FACT FINDING TOUR OF THE TROUBLESPOTS:

THIS IS SERIOUS....
...VERY SERIOUS INDEED!

REST ASSURED I'LL BE SENDING IN A TOP MAN TO GET TO THE ROOT OF THE PROBLEM!

YOU CHICKENSHIT SUBVERSIVES ARE ALL GONNA DIE!

IT'S THE REAPER!

WHO'S THE GOON WITH THE EYEBROWS, GABE?

HE'S A CANDIDATE FOR DAMNATION IF EVER THERE WAS ONE, LORD... HE TELLS LIES, HE USES BAD LANGUAGE!!

HOW ABOUT THE MAN WITH THE MUG??

HE DRINKS A LOT OF TEA, BUT HE'S CLEAN, LORD

YOU'RE GONNA LOSE, BUSTER!!

WHAAAGGH?

BUT WHY LORD? YOU DON'T EVEN VOTE LABOUR!

I CAN'T TRUST A MAN WITH EYES LIKE THAT!

IF...

The following strips appeared in the 'GUARDIAN' between Dec.1981 and June 1982

IF.... DINOSAURS ROAMED FLEET ST. 1.

Introducing:

HARRY HARDNOSE — NEWS EDITOR, 'MORNING MULE'

*@✩! TEA-BREAK STRIKE!! DID YOU EVER HEAR ANYTHING SO @ *✩!* RIDICULOUS?...

....IT'S THE @*#!✩! BRITISH DISEASE IN A *@ *✩! NUTSHELL! THESE *@ ✩ @!S ARE DESTROYING THE ECONOMY OVER TEN MINUTES TO DRINK A CUP OF *@✩!* TEA!!

S'RIGHT, HARRY!

THAT WAS A *@!* GOOD LUNCH! WHASSA *@*!✩ TIME, NOW?

ABOUT HALF PAST FOUR...

IF.... 2. DINOSAURS ROAMED FLEET ST.

introducing:

BARRY BLOCKHEAD — REPORTER

BARRY — I WANT YOU TO GET OUT THERE AND INTERVIEW IT! FIND OUT THE THINGS MR + MRS. AVERAGE PUNTER NEED TO KNOW ABOUT RAMPAGING REPTILES!

LEAVE IT OUT, HARRY — IT'S EIGHTY FEET TALL!!

OF COURSE, IF YOU'RE TURNING THE JOB DOWN....

.. HOW LONG HAVE YOU BEEN A DINOSAUR??... ...APART FROM DESTROYING BUILDINGS HAVE YOU ANY OTHER HOBBIES??.... ....WHAT DO YOU THINK OF SHIRLEY WILLIAMS??... WHAT IS YOUR FAV...

— Steve Bell —

IF...
TURKEYS DISCUSSED POLITICS
2

IF...
TURKEYS DIDN'T DISCUSS POLITICS

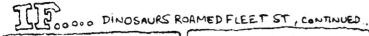

"SPOTLIGHT ON A SHAMEFUL WASTE OF PUBLIC FUNDS".....

SOUNDS VERY REASONABLE, VERA, VERY GOOD....

NEWS EDITOR — HARRY HARDNOSE

"...Not only is the use of insolent bad language common against members of the travelling public — physical attacks have been occurring regularly..."

OOOO.... TASTY, TASTY...

"...Many, whilst supposedly "on duty", were in fact engaged in DISCO DANCING SESSIONS in PUBLIC CONVENIENCES...."

WEIRD! WONDERFUL!! EAT YOUR HEART OUT, 'SUN'!! THIS IS THE REAL LOWDOWN ON THOSE ASLEF BASTARDS!!

ASLEF?? THIS IS SUPPOSED TO BE ABOUT THE POLICE!!

IF......

...FORGET ALL THIS BOLSHIE STUFF, VERA — YOU WANT TO TAKE A LEAF OUT OF BARRY'S BOOK....

SLEEEK

...HE'S GOT A "NOSE" FOR WHAT MR. + MRS AVERAGE APOLITICAL PUNTER WANT TO READ ABOUT.....

TWITCH

BARRY BLOCKHEAD INVESTIGATES

STATE SCHOOL STAFF SURPLUS SCANDAL

we expose the men and women who spend all day standing around in front of groups of children, and call it "work"..

organised DISCO DANCE SESSIONS

Kickbacks from PUPILS

"Just hanging about all day"

"Cups of Tea"

Knock off at 3.30 every day

ON HOLIDAY This is how teachers spend huge chunks of the year! — All paid for with PUBLIC MONEY.

ABROAD Some teachers actually go abroad on hol-iday...

TOMORROW

THE DOCTORS who spend all day FEELING PEOPLE UP.

NUNS ON THE SCROUNGE: PLUS: THE PRIESTS WHO WORK A ONE DAY WEEK

THE REFUSE MEN WHO REFUSE REFUSE!...

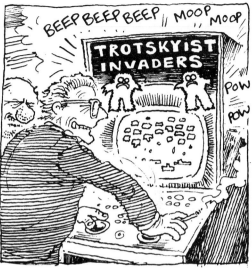

76

IF....

Panel 1: LET'S FACE IT...... WOY'S A NO-HOPER; SHIRL THE PEARL'S A WASTE OF TIME; RODGERS IS A FLABBY NITWIT; AND DOCTOR DEATH... WELL, NEED I SAY MORE??...

Panel 2: B****R THE MEMBERSHIP— WE NEED A LEADER THAT WE M.P.'s CAN TRUST!

EASY NED

@☆!! RIGHT!!

BAAARP

Panel 3: THIS IS THE FAIREST AND MOST RADICAL METHOD OF SELECTION YET DEVISED......

SPIN!

Panel 4: WHO ARE YOU, MASKED STRANGER??

IF....

Panel 5: MASKED STRANGER— YOU'VE JUST BEEN ELECTED LEADER OF THE SOCIAL DEMOCRATIC PARTY!!

GOOD GRIEF!! WHAT IS IT?

SDP

Panel 6: HAIL! HAIL TO THE CHIEF!

IT LOOKS LIKE A GIANT NEWT!

POLITE APPLAUSE

Panel 7: FINE, FINE..... WHAT SEX IS IT??

HAIL!

FLASH!

!POP!

MADAM, MAY I ASK WHY YOU'RE TRAVELLING BY BUS??....

...IT'S BECAUSE OF THE KIDS....

...THEY APPRECIATE THE FRIENDLY, HYGIENIC AND ECONOMICAL SURROUNDINGS...

...BESIDES WHICH, IT'S MY COACHMAN'S DAY OFF....

SIR, MAY I ASK WHY YOU AND YOUR FRIENDS ARE TAKING THE TUBE??

UNDERNEATH THEY'RE ALL PORKY

SURE, MAN — WE LIKE RESTRAINED ATMOSPHERE OF EASE AND PHYSICAL COMFORT.

AND WHAT ARE YOUR OCCUPATIONS?

WE'RE HEADBANGERS..

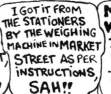

...HE SAYS THE HAMBURGERS BOTH TASTE MAGNIFICENT, BUT HE PREFERS THE ONE ON THE **RIGHT**, SEÑOR DOUCHEBAG!

...HE SAYS YOU COULD HAVE **KNOCKED** HIM DOWN WITH A **FEATHER**, SEÑOR DOUCHEBAG!!

JACK MIDDLETAR AGENT OF DESTINY

WHAT ARE THE ORDERS, COMMANDER?

WE SAIL AT DAWN!

WHO KNOWS WHAT WE'RE GETTING OURSELVES INTO THIS TIME, MR. KIPLING!

IT'S NOT EVERY DAY THE INTERNATIONAL SITUATION DEMANDS A SHOWING BY OUR ARMOURED PUNTS!

#144

steve bell

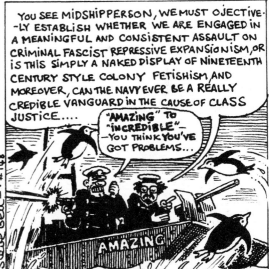

IF... NOW I NEED A FEW **ACTION-MAN-STYLE POSES**; BUT YOUR **CLOTHES** ARE **ALL WRONG**....

...WHAT DO YOU WEAR WHEN YOU WANT TO PUT THE **FRIGHTENERS** ON THE ENEMY....Y'KNOW— THE **BLACK BALACLAVA HELMETS** AND THAT SORT OF STUFF??

IF YOU'LL JUST **EXCUSE ME** A MOMENT, MR BLOCKHEAD...

NOW **LOOK HERE**, KIPLING— —THIS HAS GONE **FAR ENOUGH!!**

Steve Bell 157

IF... "INCREDIBLE" TO "REDUNDANT".... ...WE HAVE ENTERED THE WAR ZONE AND MY CREWMAN HAS **TURNED TRANSVESTITE**.... PLEASE ADVISE....

CLIK CLIK CLIK

Steve Bell—

...HE CLAIMS THAT THIS WHOLE AFFAIR IS NOTHING BUT A **STAGED MEDIA EVENT**, AND THAT BY DRESSING UP AS THE PRIME MINISTER HE IS SIMPLY MAKING A POLITICAL STATEMENT. **COULD** YOU **SUGGEST** A VIABLE COURSE OF ACTION PLEASE??

CLIK CLIK CLIK

'REDUNDANT' TO 'INCREDIBLE'... ...TRY NOT TO WORRY ABOUT IT. OVER + OUT!

158.

H.M. GOVERNMENT TRAINING STRIP.

-Steve Bell-

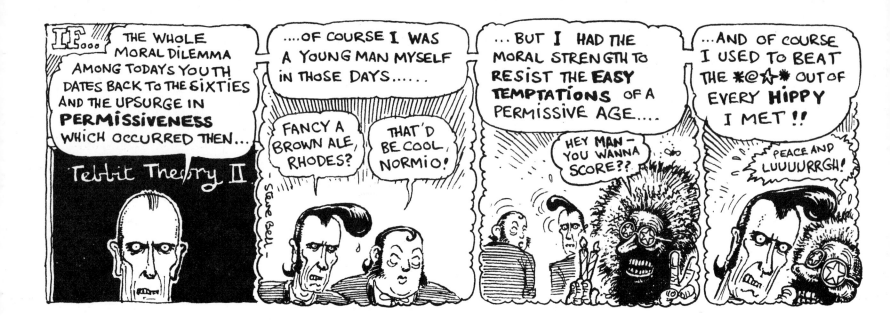

IF...

GISSANOTHER OF THESE **IRON LADIES**, BRIAN...

CARELESS TALK

Morning Mule — ARGIE LARGESSE

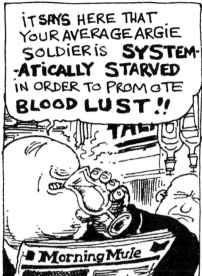
IT SAYS HERE THAT YOUR AVERAGE ARGIE SOLDIER IS **SYSTEM-ATICALLY STARVED** IN ORDER TO PROMOTE **BLOOD LUST !!**

Morning Mule

GOBLIMEY!!! WOSHOOBIN PUTTIN' IN THIS COCKTAIL??

JUST THE USUAL — ALL GOOD BRITISH INGREDIENTS

175.

I GOT THIS UNCONTROLLABLE URGE TO GO OUT AND KILL SOMEONE!!

GOOD SHOW, BADGER!

— Steve Bell —

IF...   **BEWARE CARELESS**

D'YOU WANN'EARA JOKE, BRIAN??

I'M ALWAYS GAME, BADGER!

Steve Bell — THANKS TO A.W.

WOSSA DIFFERENCE BETWEEN A **SUN REPORTER** AND A **BADLY HOUSE-TRAINED PARROT?**

WHAT'S THE DIFFERENCE BETWEEN A **SUN REPORTER** AND A **BADLY HOUSE-TRAINED PARROT??** — — I DON'T KNOW, BADGER!

I'M NOT SURPRISED.... I DON'T KNOW EITHER!...

I THINK THAT'S IN RATHER POOR TASTE, BADGER.

176

IF...

MR. KIPLING!!

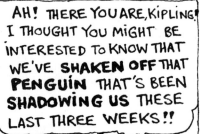

177.

DAMMIT, MAN! WHERE ARE YOU??

AH! THERE YOU ARE, KIPLING! I THOUGHT YOU MIGHT BE INTERESTED TO KNOW THAT WE'VE SHAKEN OFF THAT PENGUIN THAT'S BEEN SHADOWING US THESE LAST THREE WEEKS!!

GOD, KIPLING! HAVE YOU FINALLY TAKEN LEAVE OF YOUR SENSES?

- Steve Bell -

IF...

THIS IS REALLY TOO BAD, KIPLING! WHY ARE YOU ENGAGED IN THIS BAREFACED TREACHERY??

I'LL TELL YOU WHY, COMMANDER....IT'S SIMPLY IN ORDER TO COUNTERACT THE EFFECTS OF LONG PERIODS OF MIND-NUMBING TEDIUM PUNCTUATED BY MOMENTS OF ACUTE MORTAL TERROR.

....THIS PENGUIN IS MY FRIEND. IT'S GIVEN ME A REASON TO CARRY ON THROUGH THIS MADNESS!...

....AND BESIDES, I'VE TAUGHT IT TO SPEAK ENGLISH!!

REJOICE!!

- Steve Bell -   178.

110

111